Ant and the Break-bot

Chris Powling

Illustrated by Jon Stuart

OXFORD

In this story ...

Max

Cat

Ant

Tiger

Lucy

2

Chapter 1 – Robo-Rex Comes Alive!

Max, Cat and Tiger were on their way to Ant's house. Cat was reading the local paper. "Look at this!" she exclaimed. "It's an advert for the latest Robo-Rex movie."

ROBO-REX COMES ALIVE!

Coming soon to your local cinema. The film that will **amaze** and **thrill** you ...

"The opening night is going to be here in town," Cat went on. "All the big stars will be there … and maybe we will be there as well!"

"Us?" said Tiger. "How come?"

"Da-da!" Cat grinned.

She turned over the page.

WIN

Opening night tickets to

ROBO-REX COMES ALIVE!

AMAZING ROBOT COMPETITION!

Kids, can *you* build a robot that amazes us? Our judges will decide the best entry. The winning prize is four free tickets to see the film and meet the stars – Steve Spangler and Katie Winsome – on the opening night!

"Wow! Steve Spangler is in this movie?" said Tiger. "I'd love to meet him. We've got to win."

"It won't be easy to build the best robot," said Cat thoughtfully. "Everyone we know will want to give it a go."

"It's lucky we've got Ant to help," said Max.

Max, Cat and Tiger spotted Ant in his back garden. He was nod-nod-nodding his head and moving his hands in the air.

Cat groaned. "He's completely lost it!"

"Um … what are you doing, Ant?" said Max.

"Break-dancing," said Ant.

"*Break-dancing?*" said the others, together.

"You can't break-dance, Ant!" Tiger scoffed. "It's really hard."

"Exactly," Ant agreed. "That's why I've been practising. Look ..."

Ant popped his body.

He walked on his hands.

He flipped over backwards.

He spun round and round on his head.
"Awesome!" exclaimed Cat and Tiger.

"So, I suppose you won't have time to help us build a robot, then?" sighed Max.

"Oh, I don't know about that," said Ant. "I saw the paper, too. I haven't stopped thinking about the competition. I know exactly what sort of robot will amaze the judges …"

"What?" asked Tiger.

"A break-dancing one …"

Ant worked on the plans for making the robot. Then they all went hunting for the bits they needed for the body parts. They found some plastic tubing and metal in Ant's old toy box.

Max started with the head, Cat built the body and Tiger made the arms and legs.

"Ow! You just knocked my elbow," Cat shouted to Tiger.

"Well, you're in my way," Tiger yelled back.

They began to realize that putting a robot together wasn't easy.

Max had an idea …

14

"It would be better for us if we were smaller," said Max.

Max, Cat and Tiger pressed the dials on their watches and …

Ant stayed his proper size. He would tell them what to do.

"Right eye up a bit," Ant said to Max.

"Left arm down a bit, Cat."

"Those legs are the wrong way round," he warned Tiger.

Being micro-sized, and with Ant's help, the friends finished the robot in no time.

"Bet we are the only ones to make a robot that can break-dance," said Ant, looking pleased. "Let's call it 'Break-bot'."

"How will we power it?" Max asked.

"Micro-power!" said Ant.

"Oh, you mean …" smiled Cat.

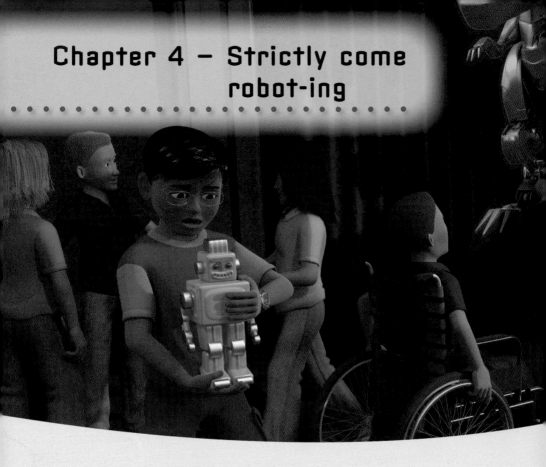

Chapter 4 – Strictly come robot-ing

The cinema was packed with children and robots. At the front, there was a model of Robo-Rex. Three judges were also on the stage, sitting behind a big desk. They were looking down at everyone.

"They make me nervous," said micro-size Tiger.

Tiger was hidden in the leg of the robot. Cat was working the arms. Max was in the head.

"Don't worry," whispered Ant. "When we're dancing, just do what I do."

Ant looked around the room. He spotted Lucy, a girl from school. She was a show-off. A crowd of people were standing around her. She was holding a sleek, shiny, pink robot.

"What's so special about her robot?" Cat wondered.

"Nothing to worry about," Ant whispered to his friends inside Break-bot.

"Are you sure?" Max said, peering through Break-bot's eyes.

Lucy had created a robot that could blow kisses every time you pressed a button on its neck.

She let every one of her friends press the button. They were amazed at how perfect the kisses were.

"Beauty-bot is by far the *best* robot," Lucy boasted. She swaggered over to her seat.

"Good morning, children!" boomed the presenter. "Welcome to the Amazing Robot Competition. Today the judges are looking for the most amazing robot – just like Robo-Rex in the new movie *Robo-Rex Comes Alive!*"

"Get ready, you guys," Ant muttered.

Chapter 5 – The break-dance

There were lots of children in the competition. They each presented their robot to the judges.

There was one robot that could wink, one that could talk, one that shuffled forwards ... but then fell over.

Soon it was Lucy's turn. She came up to the stage and gave a little curtsey.

"This is Beauty-bot," she told the judges, sweetly. Lucy pressed the button. Oh dear … something went wrong. Instead of blowing a kiss, it made a rude noise. Lucy's face went bright red.

Luckily, the judges had a sense of humour.

"Well, that certainly amazed me!" laughed one of the judges.

"And me," agreed another.

Now it was Ant's turn. "This is it!" whispered Ant to Break-bot, stepping forwards.

"I'm a break-dancer," he explained to the judges, "so is Break-bot – the robot I've built. We've worked out a dance together."

"Let's see it," said the judge nearest him.

No one knew that Max, Cat and Tiger were inside the robot.

When Ant popped his body, Break-bot popped its body. When Ant walked on his hands, Break-bot walked on its hands. Whatever Ant did, Break-bot did, too. Every kid in the place could see that Ant's robot was bound to be the winner.

At least, until …

... Break-bot fell apart.

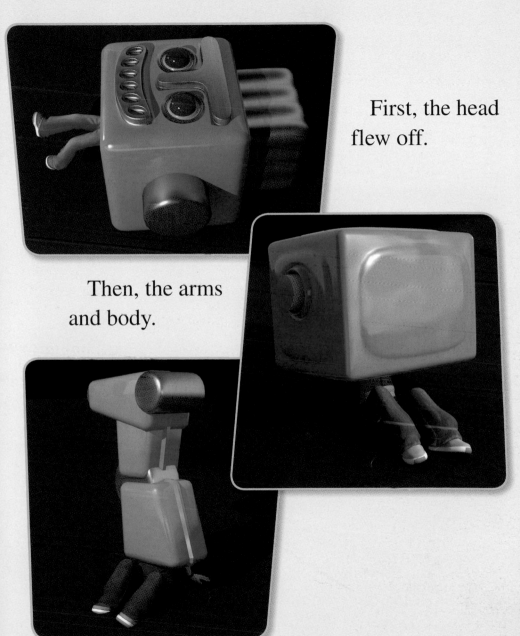

First, the head flew off.

Then, the arms and body.

Finally, the legs and feet collapsed.

By that time, the whole cinema was rocking with laughter.

"I've never seen a break-dancer actually break!" said one judge, wiping his eyes. "What a shame there's no robot left. We can't possibly give it the prize."

Chapter 6 – Another surprise from Ant

The next day Max, Cat and Tiger met in the micro-den. They were really disappointed.

"It's our fault," said Max miserably. "We should have spent more time testing it."

"Well, I suppose we did *nearly* win the competition," said Cat.

"Pity Lucy won," Tiger sighed. "Mind you, her Beauty-bot didn't work quite how she wanted."

"Hey!" said Ant, as he clambered into the micro-den. "Why are you looking so sad?"

"What's there to be happy about?" Max asked.

"Well, read this e-mail!" Ant beamed.

He handed them a bit of paper he had printed off.

Dear Ant,

We're really sorry we couldn't make you the winner yesterday. However, we think that Break-bot was really amazing, so we are sending you free passes to see the film studio where *Robo-Rex Comes Alive!* was made. You'll also meet Steve Spangler and Katie Winsome, of course!

Best wishes,
The Judges
Amazing Robot Competition

Max, Cat, Ant and Tiger didn't say a word for the next five minutes. They were too busy doing the most amazing break-dance ever.